balancing life's demands

BIBLICAL PRIORITIES FOR A BUSY LIFE

CHIP INGRAM

Balancing Life's Demands

TABLE OF CONTENTS

SMALL GROUP

The fact that you are even reading this page says a lot about you. It says that you are either one of those people that has to read everything, or you are at least open to being used by God to lead a group.

Leading a small group can sound intimidating, but it really doesn't have to be. Think of it more as gathering a few friends to get to know each other better and to have some discussion around spiritual matters.

Here are a few practical tips to help you get started:

1. **PRAY**
   One of the most important principles of spiritual leadership is to realize you can't do this on your own. No matter how long we've been leading, we need the power of the Holy Spirit. Lean on Him... He will help you.

2. **INVITE SOME FRIENDS**
   Don't be afraid to ask people to come to your group. You will be surprised how many people are open to such a study, especially when you let them know that the study is only for eight weeks. Whether you have 4 of 14 in your group, it can be a powerful experience. You should probably plan on at least an hour and a half for your group meeting.

3. **GET YOUR MATERIALS**
   You will need to get a DVD of the video teaching done by Chip Ingram. You can get the DVD from LivingontheEdge.org. Also, it will be helpful for each person to have their own study guide. You can also purchase those through the website.

4. **BE PREPARED TO FACILITATE**
   Just a few minutes a week in preparation can make a huge difference in the group experience. Each week preview the video teaching and review the discussion questions. If you don't think your group can get through all the questions, select the ones that are most relevant to your group.

5. **LOVE YOUR GROUP**
   Maybe the most important thing you bring to the group is your personal care for them. If you will pray for them, encourage them, call them, e-mail them, involve them, and love them, God will be pleased and you will have a lot of fun along the way.

how to get the most out of this

EXPERIENCE

You and your group are about to begin what could be a life-changing journey in your small group. This practical series will help you and your group discover God's plan for handling life's challenges.

Listed below are the segments you will experience each week as well as some hints for getting the most out of this experience.

TAKE IT IN: During this section you will watch the video teaching. Each teaching segment is about 25 minutes long. A teaching outline with fill-ins is provided for each session. As you follow along, write down questions or insights that you can share during the discussion time. Also, bring your Bible each week.

TALK IT OVER: Several discussion questions are provided for your group to further engage the teaching content. Keep the following guidelines in mind for having a healthy group discussion.

- Be involved. Jump in and share your thoughts. Your ideas are important, and you have a perspective that is unique and can benefit the other group members.

- Be a good listener. Value what others are sharing. Seek to really understand the perspective of others in your group and don't be afraid to ask follow up questions.

- Be courteous. Always treat others with utmost respect. When there is disagreement, focus on the issue and never turn the discussion into a personal attack.

- Be focused. Stay on topic. Help the group explore the subject at hand, and try to save unrelated questions or stories for afterwards.

- Be careful not to dominate. Be aware of the amount of talking you are doing in proportion to the rest of the group, and make space for others to speak.

- Be a learner. Stay sensitive to what God might be wanting to teach you through the lesson, as well as through what others have to say.

LIVE IT OUT: These simple suggestions help the lesson come to life. Don't ignore them; give them a try! Check in with another group member during the week and ask how it's going.

the peace and power of a prioritized life

SESSION  1

**³³But seek first his kingdom and his righteousness,
and all these things will be given to you as well.**

MATTHEW 6:33 (NIV)

six symptoms of misplaced priorities

1. _____ — The Activity Trap

**"Emotion is no substitute for action and action
is no substitute for productivity."**

DAWSON TROTMAN

2. _____ stress and pressure

Can end up in burnout, breakdown or blow up

3. Low grade _____

4. _____ debt

5. _____ —"leakage in your devotional life"

6. _____ behavior

an overview of biblical priorities

Sometimes the structure of a book can tell you as much as the content.

Topic	Colossians	Ephesians
God	3:1-7	5:1-20
Mate	3:18-19	5:21-33
Family	3:20-21	6:1-4
Work	3:22-4:1	6:5-9
Ministry	4:2-6	6:10-20

Don't think of priorities as "_____"

> **Jesus answered, "Everyone who drinks this water will be thirsty again, [14]but whoever drinks the water I give him will never thirst. Indeed, the water I give him will become in him a spring of water welling up to eternal life."**
>
> *JOHN 4:13-14 (NIV)*

> **[23]Watch over your heart with all diligence, for from it flow the springs of life.**
>
> *PROVERBS 4:23 (NASB)*

> **The urgent is rarely important and the important is rarely urgent.**
>
> *DWIGHT EISENHOWER*

❶❶ TALK IT OVER

1. Of the six symptoms of misplaced priorities that Chip mentioned, which one do you struggle with the most? Why?

_____

_____

_____

2. Where does life feel most out of balance right now?

_____

_____

_____

3. The first symptom Chip talked about was busyness. Describe your pace of life and busyness over the last 60 days. Is it out of control? Manageable? Exhausting? Healthy?

_____

_____

_____

4. On the dashboard of your life, how would your emotional and financial gauges read? Place a mark on each gauge that honestly depicts where you are today. Then, share with the group why you marked your gauges as you did.

_____

_____

_____

5. What one step could you take that would make you even healthier (and less stressed) when it comes to emotions and/or finances?

_____

_____

_____

6. Dwight Eisenhower said "The urgent is rarely important and the important is rarely urgent." What important (not urgent) priority do you need to focus on?

_____

_____

_____

7. Jesus said [33]But seek first his kingdom and his righteousness, and all these things will be given to you as well. Matthew 6:33 (NIV)

    For you, what does "seeking first the kingdom" look like?

_____

_____

_____

✪ LIVE IT OUT

Have an unhurried conversation with a spouse or friend this week about "what's most important" and "what gets in the way" of living for what's most important.

the peace and power of a prioritized life

PART 2

SESSION 2

Two Tools of a Prioritized Life

1. Your _____

> The length of our days is seventy years—
> or eighty, if we have the strength;
> yet their span is but trouble and sorrow,
> for they quickly pass, and we fly away.
> 11Who knows the power of your anger?
> For your wrath is as great as the fear that is due you.
> 12Teach us to number our days aright,
> that we may gain a heart of wisdom.
>
> *PSALM 90:10-12 (NIV)*

> 15Therefore be careful how you walk, not as unwise men but as wise,
> 16making the most of your time, because the days are evil.
> 17So then do not be foolish, but understand
> what the will of the Lord is.
>
> *EPHESIANS 5:15-17 (NASB)*

v. 16 "time" = _____ of opportunity

Principle — Do what matters most _____.

Application

Where to start...

- For a new Christian—The book of Mark
- For an older Christian—The book of James

2PROAPT — 20 minutes a day

P — Pray

P — Preview

R — Read

O — Observe

A — Apply

P — Pray

T — Tell

2. Your _____

Your money reflects your _____.

> **⁹Honor the LORD with your wealth,**
> **with the firstfruits of all your crops;**
> **¹⁰then your barns will be filled to overflowing,**
> **and your vats will brim over with new wine.**
>
> *PROVERBS 3:9-10 (NIV)*

How Do You Get Your Money Under Control

1. Give the first portion of each paycheck to the Lord.

2. Pay your bills next

3. Live on the rest

4. Get out of debt

Very early in the morning, while it was still dark, Jesus got up, left the house and went off to a solitary place, where he prayed.

MARK 1:35 (NIV)

TALK IT OVER

1. With regards to my time and money, on a scale of 1-5, how am I doing?

    1 | | | 2 | | | 3 | | | 4 | | | 5
    Not so good   *Good*   *Great*

2. The New Living Translation of Psalm 90:12 says Teach us to realize the brevity of life so that we may grow in wisdom. How does realizing the brevity of life help us grow in wisdom? How would you describe yourself when it comes to managing your time well?

    _____

    _____

    _____

3. Who do you know that lived their life well and finished well? What did you most respect and admire about them?

    _____

    _____

    _____

4. Paul challenged us in Ephesians 5 to make the most of our time because the days are evil. What practical step could you take to "make the most of your time"?

_____

_____

_____

5. How are you doing at consistently spending time with God in his word? What could make that time more consistent and more fruitful?

_____

_____

_____

6. When you were growing up, how did your family handle money? Were they frugal? careless? generous? planners? materialistic? How did your family's attitude toward money impact you?

_____

_____

_____

7. Chip talked about four ways to get your money under control. Which one do you most struggle with?

_____

_____

_____

⊕ LIVE IT OUT

At least 5 days this week set aside 20 minutes per day to spend time with God in His word. Use the 2PROAPT process that Chip described.

how to put first things first

three reasons why most of us live with two sets of priorities:

1. We are _____. We honestly don't see the discrepancy between what we think and say, and how we actually live.

2. We are _____. Though we long to put "first things first," we simply do not believe that God will supply our needs if we give Him the first portion of our time, our lives, and our money.

3. We have _____ repeatedly. Our sincere and honest efforts to put "first things first" in the past lasted only a short time and ended with frustration and disillusionment with ourselves.

What is the "Missing Ingredient" to Living Out Our Priorities?

- It's a _____ used word.

- It's a _____ of the Spirit.

- It comes to us by _____.

- We _____ it in others.

- It's _____ for putting "first things first."

- The key word is _____

DEFINITION: Discipline is doing what needs to be done when it needs to be done.

truths about discipline

- Discipline is the Spirit-empowered ability given by God's grace that allows us to say "no" to the quick fix and the easy road, and say "yes" to the harder but better way.

11For the grace of God that brings salvation has appeared to all men. 12It teaches us to say "No" to ungodliness and worldly passions, and to live self-controlled, upright and godly lives in this present age,

TITUS 2:11-12 (NIV)

- Grace _____ discipline

- Grace _____ us

- Discipline is a by-product of the _____ work in our lives.

22But the fruit of the Spirit is love, joy, peace, patience, kindness, goodness, faithfulness, 23gentleness and self-control. Against such things there is no law.

GALATIANS 5:22-23 (NIV)

- We are _____ to live disciplined lives.

6and to knowledge, self-control; and to self-control, perseverance; and to perseverance, godliness;

2 PETER 1:6 (NIV)

- Discipline is a _____ that is learned over time through training.

The Dynamics of Biblical Discipline Can Be Summed Up in 2 Words:

_____   _____

> **All discipline for the moment seems not to be joyful,
> but sorrowful; yet to those who have been trained by it,
> afterwards it yields the peaceful fruit of righteousness.**
>
> *HEBREWS 12:11 (NASB)*

> **"Discipline is willfully choosing to embrace the painful and
> difficult aspects of one's life... first, in order to more fully enjoy and
> successfully achieve those relationships that mean the most."**
>
> *M. SCOTT PECK*

🕛 TALK IT OVER

1. Think back to your childhood. When you were growing up, was discipline (self-control) an important value in your home? Share an example of an area where your family was disciplined or lacked discipline.

   _____

   _____

   _____

2. Share about an area of your life where you have been successful in being disciplined?

   _____

   _____

   _____

3. If you were mentoring a college student about discipline, what lessons have you learned about discipline (self-control) that you would pass on?

_____

_____

_____

4. Chip said "grace produces discipline". How does grace produce discipline in our lives? (Go back to Titus 2:11-12)

_____

_____

_____

5. What is the difference between "trying hard" and "training"? How does this apply to the Christian life?

_____

_____

_____

6. In what priority area of your life do you need to be more disciplined? What could be the positive results of more discipline in that area?

_____

_____

_____

7. What steps could you take this week to have more discipline in that area?

_____

_____

_____

🌍 LIVE IT OUT

Have an honest conversation this week with a friend about this issue of discipline (self-control). Ask them for their help and come up with specific ways they can support you and keep you accountable.

how to put first things first

PART 2

The Method of Developing Biblical Discipline: _____

_____ Decision-Making

• The Biblical Example – the Apostle Paul

²⁴Do you not know that those who run in a race all run, but only one receives the prize? Run in such a way that you may win. ²⁵And everyone who competes in the games exercises self-control in all things. They then (do it) to receive a perishable wreath, but we an imperishable. ²⁶Therefore I run in such a way, as not without aim; I box in such a way, as not beating the air; ²⁷but I buffet my body and make it my slave, lest possibly, after I have preached to others, I myself should be disqualified.

1 CORINTHIANS 9:24-27 (NASB)

• How Did It Work For Paul?

He had a clear cut _____ — to win. (v.24)

He was focused on the _____. (v.25)

He had an _____ motive (v.25-26)

• How Does It Work For Us?

1. Advanced Decision Making begins with clear-cut

   _____.

2. Advanced Decision Making is reinforced by focusing on the

   _____.

3. Advanced Decision Making becomes a personal conviction when you

   ponder the _____.

💬 TALK IT OVER

1. Chip shared some areas where he has made some decisions in advance. Where do you need to apply the principle of advance decision making? Get specific and practical.

    _____

    _____

    _____

2. Read 1 Corinthians 9:24-27. What stands out to you from this passage? What from this passage most applies to you today?

    _____

    _____

    _____

3. Read Philippians 3:12-14. What can we learn from Paul in this passage about priorities and keeping "first things first"?

    _____

    _____

    _____

4. If you were developing a "to be" list, what would be on your list?

    _____

    _____

    _____

5. Chip talked about putting his "to be" list on his calendar. Select one items that would be on your "to be" list and share what it would look like for you to work that into your schedule.

_____

_____

_____

6. Think of an area where you want to be more disciplined. What would it look like to apply the principle of "focusing on the reward".

_____

_____

_____

7. What consequence of "blowing it" scares you to death?

_____

_____

_____

✪ LIVE IT OUT

Carve out a little time this week to get alone with God. Get some 3x5 cards and begin to write out the desires of your heart about who you want "to be".

how to keep first things first

PART 1

SESSION  **5**

the problem: many start well, but few finish well.

The Answer: Biblical _____

Definition: Biblical Accountability is enlisting the support of those who love me to help me keep my commitments to God.

> **As iron sharpens iron, so one man sharpens another.**
>
> *PROVERBS 27:17 (NIV)*

> **⁹Two are better than one, because they have a good return for their work: ¹⁰If one falls down, his friend can help him up. But pity the man who falls and has no one to help him up! ¹¹Also, if two lie down together, they will keep warm. But how can one keep warm alone? ¹²Though one may be overpowered, two can defend themselves. A cord of three strands is not quickly broken.**
>
> *ECCLESIASTES 4:9-12 (NIV)*

You cannot do the Christian life _____.

five reasons why accountability is essential for spiritual success

1. Because we never _____ the need for personal accountability.

²⁴Do you not know that those who run in a race all run, but only one receives the prize? Run in such a way that you may win. ²⁵Everyone who competes in the games exercises self-control in all things. They then do it to receive a perishable wreath, but we an imperishable. ²⁶Therefore I run in such a way, as not without aim; I box in such a way, as not beating the air; ²⁷but I discipline my body and make it my slave, so that, after I have preached to others, I myself will not be disqualified.

1 CORINTHIANS 9:24-27 (NASB)

The more responsibility you get, the more _____ you need.

2. Because past successes are no guarantee of future _____.

Your spiritual _____ will not sustain you.

¹For I do not want you to be unaware, brethren, that our fathers were all under the cloud and all passed through the sea; ²and all were baptized into Moses in the cloud and in the sea; ³and all ate the same spiritual food; ⁴and all drank the same spiritual drink, for they were drinking from a spiritual rock which followed them; and the rock was Christ. ⁵Nevertheless, with most of them God was not well-pleased; for they were laid low in the wilderness.

1 CORINTHIANS 10:1-5 (NASB)

Walking with God in the past is no guarantee that you'll walk with him in the future.

𝟸𝟸 TALK IT OVER

1. When have you experienced appropriate/positive accountability? What were the results?

2. Where do you need accountability in your life right now?

3. What are some common fears and roadblocks that keep people from pursuing accountability.

4. In what ways has American individualism influenced Christians in our generation? In what ways does it show up in your own life?

5. The Bible expects us to be connected to "one another". Use your Bibles and come up with a list of the "one anothers" in Scripture.

    Which of these "one anothers" does your group need to work on?

    _____

    _____

    _____

6. Chip said "the more responsibility one gets, the more accountability that you need." Why is that true?

    _____

    _____

    _____

7. The Bible says that we are to "spur one another on toward love and good deeds." (Hebrews 10:24 NIV) Complete the following statement. "This group could spur me on in my spiritual growth by..."

    _____

    _____

    _____

⊘ LIVE IT OUT

Do a study this week of all the "one another" verses in the Bible. Identify one or two that you want to work on over the next few days.

how to keep first things first

PART 2

SESSION **6**

five reasons why accountability is essential for spiritual success

1. Because we never outgrow the need for personal accountability. (Covered in Session 5)

2. Because past successes are no guarantee of future faithfulness. (Covered in Session 5)

3. Because we constantly underestimate the power of our own

   _____.

> Now these things happened as examples for us, so that we would not crave evil things as they also craved. ⁷Do not be idolaters, as some of them were; as it is written, "The people sat to eat and drink and stood to play." ⁸Nor let us act immorally, as some of them did, and twenty-three thousand fell in one day. ⁹Nor let us try the Lord, as some of them did, and were destroyed by the serpents. ¹⁰Nor grumble, as some of them did, and were destroyed by the destroyer. ¹¹Now these things happened to them as an example, and they were written for our instruction, upon whom the ends of the ages have come.
>
> *1 CORINTHIANS 10:6-11 (NASB)*

4. Because we constantly overestimate our ability to handle

   _____.

> Therefore let him who thinks he stands take heed that he does not fall.
>
> *1 CORINTHIANS 10:12 (NASB)*

But encourage one another day after day, as long as it is still called "Today," so that none of you will be hardened by the deceitfulness of sin.

HEBREWS 3:13 (NASB)

5.   Because we naively believe our struggles and temptations are

_____.

No temptation has overtaken you but such as is common to man; and God is faithful, who will not allow you to be tempted beyond what you are able, but with the temptation will provide the way of escape also, so that you will be able to endure it.

1 CORINTHIANS 10:13 (NASB)

SUMMARY: "Therefore, my beloved, flee from _____!"
                1 Corinthians 10:14 (NASB)

the means: "how to" develop accountability in relationships:

- It begins at _____.

- In an atmosphere of _____.

- It must be voluntary and by _____.

- It must be _____, not generic.

- It must be regular, not sporadic.

- No more than _____.

Making sincere commitments is tough...

        Keeping them is next to impossible _____

🔊 TALK IT OVER

1. Of the six steps Chip mentions for developing accountability, which one is most applicable to you?

_____

_____

_____

2. What are the qualities you want in someone you invite to help you be accountable?

_____

_____

_____

3. What are some practical ways that a trusted friend could help us when we are facing temptation?

_____

_____

_____

4. Chip began this session by warning us about underestimating our sinful passions. What biblical stories can you think of where people underestimated their sinful passions?

_____

_____

_____

5. Proverbs 24:26 (NIV) says An honest answer is like a kiss on the lips. And Proverbs 27:5-6 (NIV) says An open rebuke is better than hidden love! Wounds from a sincere friend are better than many kisses from an enemy.

Share a time when you benefited from a wound from a sincere friend.

_____

_____

_____

6. James 5:16 (NIV) says Therefore confess your sins to each other and pray for each other so that you may be healed. The prayer of a righteous man is powerful and effective. How does confessing our sins to each other lead to healing?

_____

_____

_____

7. How would you describe the level of authentic accountability that you currently have in your life? Are there steps you should take to take this more seriously?

_____

_____

_____

⊗ LIVE IT OUT

This week write out a list of accountability questions that would be helpful for someone to ask you.

warning: personal discipline can be hazardous to your health

PART 1

biblical priorities "pop quiz"

To what degree have you taken specific steps in the following areas?

(1 = none; 2 = little; 3 = started and doing okay; 4 = making good progress; 5 = vigorously pursuing)

___ Objectives: Moving from vague ideas to specific decisions about the kind of person I want to become and what I want to accomplish.

___ Priorities: Ordering my life in such a way that the important and eternal are not forfeited by the "pressing" and the "urgent."

___ Schedule: Determining specifically how and when I will place the important and eternal in my daily life.

___ Discipline: Doing what needs to be done when it needs to be done (i.e. choosing to habitually delay gratification of short-term pleasures in order to more fully enjoy long-term success).

___ Accountability: Enlisting the support of those who love me to help me keep my commitments to God.

___ *TOTAL SCORE*

jesus' warning #1:

In our pursuit of "seeking first" His righteousness there is the...

...danger of _____.

MATTHEW 5 OVERVIEW

The reward and character of true Christ followers
5:3-12

Salt and light — be worthy examples
5:13-16

Relationship of this new teaching to the Law of Moses
5:17-20

TRUE RIGHTEOUSNESS
(Matthew 5:20)

"You have heard it said...	*but I say to you..."*
External	**Internal**
Doing	Being
Duty	Devotion
Performance	Relationship
Guilt	Grace
Letter	Spirit
Head	Heart

True righteousness is about relationship, not _____.

The application of Matthew 5:20 to...

- Murder — 5:21-26
- Adultery — 5:27-30
- Divorce — 5:31-32
- Oaths — 5:33-37
- Retribution — 5:38-42
- Enemies — 5:43-48

SUMMARY: Jesus condemns _____ righteousness (spiritual

activities) when it does not flow from _____

relationship with God.

43

1. From the pop quiz, which area got the best score and which one do you need to work on? Is there anything you sense God is prompting you to do about this area?

_____

_____

_____

2. Chip said that Matthew 5:3-12 defines the characteristics of an authentic follower of Christ. Read that passage again and share which quality you think would have most shocked the Pharisees.

_____

_____

_____

3. Read Matthew 5:13-16. Why are salt and light good word pictures to describe the influence of believers?

_____

_____

_____

4. Chip said "true righteousness is always an issue of relationship, not performance". Think back to the early days of your faith. Was the focus more on relationship or rules? Share what or who influenced your perspective.

_____

_____

_____

5. How has your understanding of "true righteousness" changed?

    _____

    _____

    _____

6. Read Matthew 23:1-7. What would be the modern day equivalent for some of the things Jesus condemns in this passage?

    _____

    _____

    _____

7. What are some practical things you can do to make sure your faith is internal (relationship) and not just external (performance)?

    _____

    _____

    _____

✪ LIVE IT OUT

Spend some time this week reading and reflecting on Matthew 23. Ask God to give you a heightened awareness when you begin to act and think like a Pharisee.

warning: personal discipline can be hazardous to your health

PART 2

jesus' warning #1:

In our pursuit of "seeking first" His righteousness there is the...

danger of distortion. (covered in session 7)

jesus' warning #2:

In our pursuit of "seeking first" His righteousness there is also the...

danger of _____. (Matthew 6:1-18)

- **Giving** — Key Issue = _____ Matthew 6:1- 4

  Giving guards your _____.

- **Prayer** — Key Issue = _____ Matthew 6:5-8

  Prayer guards your _____.

- **Fasting** — Key Issue = _____ Matthew 6:16-18

  Fasting guards your _____.

SUMMARY: Spiritual disciplines are _____
but become dangerous when they become a means to
gain the _____ of men rather
than deepen our relationship with God.

Application: _____ is God's method of keeping our motives pure.

You are those who justify yourselves in the sight of men, but God knows your heart; for that which is highly esteemed among men is detestable in the sight of God.

LUKE 16:15 (NIV)

Am I now trying to win the approval of men, or of God? Or am I trying to please men? If I were still trying to please men I would not be a servant of Christ.

GALATIANS 1:10 (NIV)

ⓙ TALK IT OVER

1. Share about the time in your life when you were most in love with Jesus, share when and why.

    _____

    _____

    _____

2. Chip talked a lot about motives in this session. When are you most apt to do something out of an impure motive?

    _____

    _____

    _____

3. Read Luke 18:9-14. What is it about the prayer of the Pharisee that Jesus rebukes? What is it about the prayer of the tax collector that Jesus affirms?

    _____

    _____

    _____

4. Read Matthew 6:1-4. We may not blow the trumpet to announce our good deeds, but what are some subtle ways that we can "toot our own horn" when doing good deeds?

    _____

    _____

    _____

5. Read Matthew 6:5-8. How should this passage change how we pray as individuals and as a small group?

_____

_____

_____

6. Chip said "Spiritual disciplines are essential but become dangerous when they become a means to gain the reward of men rather than deepen our relationship with God." What steps can you take in your practice of spiritual disciplines to make sure you are not seeking the reward of men?

_____

_____

_____

7. Read Matthew 6:16-18 and Isaiah 58:3-7. What can we learn from these two passages about fasting in a way that pleases God?

_____

_____

_____

☉ LIVE IT OUT

Consider doing a 24 hour fast this week. Apply what you learned from Matthew 6 this week about motives and not doing things for the reward of men.

how to escape the rat race forever

Are you "clearing cobwebs" or "killing spiders"?

The root problem in priority living according to Jesus is _____.

Materialism is a disease of both the rich and the poor and everyone in between.

Materialism is a condition of the heart where I am leaning, trusting, depending, or even believing that the outward props of things, money, and possessions and the fame, status, and power that they provide have the ability to achieve for me inward peace, happiness and satisfaction in my life.

Materialism is a condition of the _____.

Instruct those who are rich in this present world not to be conceited or to fix their hope on the uncertainty of riches, but on God, who richly supplies us with all things to enjoy.

1 TIMOTHY 6:17 (NASB)

MATTHEW 6:1-18

Two Motives

↓

Two Treasures

¹⁹"Do not store up for yourselves treasures on earth, where moth and rust destroy, and where thieves break in and steal. ²⁰But store up for yourselves treasures in heaven, where moth and rust do not destroy, and where thieves do not break in and steal. ²¹For where your treasure is, there your heart will be also.

MATTHEW 6:19-21 (NIV)

Your money is the greatest, clearest, true _____ of your heart.

Our trust always follows our _____.

> 22"The eye is the lamp of the body. If your eyes are good,
> your whole body will be full of light. 23But if your eyes are
> bad, your whole body will be full of darkness. If then the
> light within you is darkness, how great is that darkness!
>
> *MATTHEW 6:22-23 (NIV)*

Your outlook will determine your outcome.

Your perception will determine your pursuits.

There are two motives in walking with God...those two motives lead to your treasure...
what treasure you pursue has to do with your core beliefs, passions and desires.

> 24"No one can serve two masters. Either he will hate the
> one and love the other, or he will be devoted to the one and
> despise the other. You cannot serve both God and Money.
>
> *MATTHEW 6:24 (NIV)*

SUMMARY: Do not allow the pursuit of material things to thwart your

_____ development.

QUESTION: How can we live in a material world without becoming materialistic?

[24]"No one can serve two masters. Either he will hate the one and love the other, or he will be devoted to the one and despise the other. You cannot serve both God and Money. [25]Therefore I tell you, do not worry about your life, what you will eat or drink; or about your body, what you will wear. Is not life more important than food, and the body more important than clothes? [26]Look at the birds of the air; they do not sow or reap or store away in barns, and yet your heavenly Father feeds them. Are you not much more valuable than they? [27]Who of you by worrying can add a single hour to his life?"

MATTHEW 6:24-27 (NIV)

[28]"And why do you worry about clothes? See how the lilies of the field grow. They do not labor or spin. [29]Yet I tell you that not even Solomon in all his splendor was dressed like one of these. [30]If that is how God clothes the grass of the field, which is here today and tomorrow is thrown into the fire, will he not much more clothe you, O you of little faith? [31]So do not worry, saying, 'What shall we eat?' or 'What shall we drink?' or 'What shall we wear?' [32]For the pagans run after all these things, and your heavenly Father knows that you need them."

MATTHEW 6:28-32 (NIV)

🕕 TALK IT OVER

1. All of us are influenced by our past. How was money talked about and modeled and how has that influenced your life?

    _____

    _____

    _____

2. How does materialism impact people having margin in their lives? What possession in your life eats away at margin?

_____

_____

_____

3. Read 1 Timothy 6:17. Which part of Paul's challenge most speaks to you personally?

_____

_____

_____

4. Chip said "people whose God is gold always have anxiety". Why does materialism lead to anxiety and worry in our lives?

_____

_____

_____

5. How can we live in a material world without being materialistic?

_____

_____

_____

6. Read Luke 12:13-21. When you hear this story from Jesus, what is your personal "takeaway"?

_____

_____

_____

7. What can you do practically to kill the spider of materialism in your life?

_____

_____

_____

☺ LIVE IT OUT

As a way to disarm materialism in your life, this week give away something you own. Bless someone else by giving them something valuable.

how to escape the rat race forever

PART 2

SESSION 10

> ³³"But seek first His kingdom and His righteousness, and all these things will be given to you as well. ³⁴Therefore do not worry about tomorrow, for tomorrow will worry about itself. Each day has enough trouble of its own."
>
> *MATTHEW 6:33-34 (NIV)*

THE SYMPTOM: Anxiety is the mark of a life preoccupied with material things.

The acid test of materialism is not how much I have or don't have but my preoccupation and concern over it.

THE EXPLANATION: Stop your preoccupation with material things because...

1. It's _____

> **Therefore I tell you, do not worry about your life, what you will eat or drink; or about your body, what you will wear. Is not life more important than food, and the body more important than clothes?**
>
> *MATTHEW 6:25 (NIV)*

2. It's _____

> **Look at the birds of the air; they do not sow or reap or store away in barns, and yet your heavenly Father feeds them. Are you not much more valuable than they?**
>
> **And why do you worry about clothes? See how the lilies of the field grow. They do not labor or spin. ²⁹Yet I tell you that not even Solomon in all his splendor was dressed like one of these. ³⁰If that is how God clothes the grass of the field, which is here today and tomorrow is thrown into the fire, will he not much more clothe you, O you of little faith?**
>
> *MATTHEW 6:26, 28-30 (NIV)*

3. It's _____

Who of you by worrying can add a single hour to his life?

MATTHEW 6:27 (NIV)

4. It's _____ to God

If that is how God clothes the grass of the field, which is here today and tomorrow is thrown into the fire, will he not much more clothe you, O you of little faith? 31So do not worry, saying, 'What shall we eat?' or 'What shall we drink?' or 'What shall we wear?' 32For the pagans run after all these things, and your heavenly Father knows that you need them.

MATTHEW 6:30-32 (NIV)

THE PROMISE: Matthew 6:33-34
If you will pursue knowing Christ and making Him known as your first priority, He will meet all your material needs.

APPLICATION: Questions to Ponder

- Are you "spending" or "investing" your life?

- Is your life making a significant difference in the lives of others?

- Do you live under "pressure" or under "priorities"?

- Does your time, talent, and treasure reflect that pursuing Christ and making Him known is your #1 priority?

⏷ TALK IT OVER

1. What one change, if you actually made it, would help you live out what you have learned from this series?

    _____

    _____

    _____

2. The acid test of materialism is not how much I have or don't have but my preoccupation and concern over material things. As you think about your life in recent weeks, describe your level of preoccupation and concern over material things.

    _____

    _____

    _____

3. Chip talked about the crazy pace of the "rat race". What would it look like for your family to have a more sane rhythm of life?

    _____

    _____

    _____

4. How could you simplify your life and make it less dependent on "things"? What do you need to cut loose?

    _____

    _____

    _____

5. How does "trusting God" help you in the battle of materialism?

6. Read Matthew 6:26-30. What are you worried about right now that you need to trust God for?

7. Chip said to "invest in people and use things to extend love". Since relationships are most important, what relationship do you need to invest in?

⊘ LIVE IT OUT

Have a conversation with your family or a close friend this week about making the necessary changes to balance life's demands. Put together a game plan. Get serious about putting what you've learned into action.

leader's notes

GROUP AGREEMENT

People come to groups with a variety of different expectations. The purpose of a group agreement is simply to make sure everyone is on the same page and that we have some common expectations. The following group agreement is a tool to help the group discuss specific guidelines together during your first meeting. Modify anything that does not work for your group, then be sure to discuss the questions that follow. This will help you to have an even greater group experience!

we agree to the following priorities

- Take the Bible Seriously — to seek to understand and apply God's truth in the Bible

- Group Attendance — to give priority to the group meeting
  (Call if I am going to be absent or late.)

- Safe Environment — to create a safe place where people can be heard and feel loved (no snap judgments or simple fixes)

- Be Confidential — to keep anything that is shared strictly confidential and within the group

- Spiritual Health — to give group members permission to help me live a godly, healthy spiritual life that is pleasing to God

- Building Relationships — to get to know the other members of the group and pray for them regularly

- Prayer — to regularly pray with and for each other

- Other

  _____

  _____

OUR GAME PLAN

- Will we have refreshments?

  _____

  _____

- What will we do about childcare?

  _____

  _____

- What day and time will we meet?

  _____

  _____

- Where will we meet?

  _____

  _____

- How long will we meet each week?

  _____

  _____

HOW TO MAKE THIS A MEANINGFUL EXPERIENCE FOR YOUR GROUP

BEFORE THE GROUP ARRIVES

1. **Be prepared.** Your personal preparation can make a huge difference in the quality of the group experience. We strongly suggest previewing both the DVD teaching program by Chip Ingram along with the accompanying parts of the study guide.

2. **Pray for your group members by name.** Ask God to use your time together to touch the heart of every person in your group. Expect God to challenge and change people as a result of this study.

3. **Provide refreshments.** There's nothing like food to help a group relax and connect with each other. For the first week, we suggest you prepare a snack, but after that, ask other group members to bring the food so that they share in the responsibilities of the group and make a commitment to return.

4. **Relax.** Don't try to imitate someone else's style of leading a group. Lead the group in a way that fits your style and temperament. Remember that people may feel a bit nervous showing up for a small group study, so put them at ease when they arrive. Make sure to have all the details covered prior to your group meeting, so that once people start arriving, you can focus on greeting them.

❤ TAKE IT IN   watch the video

1. **Arrange the room.** Set up the chairs in the room so that everyone can see the television. It's best to arrange the room in such a way that it is conducive to discussion.

2. **Get the video ready.** Each video session on the DVD has 3 components. During the first 2-3 minutes, Chip introduces this week's topic. Then, the group will watch the actual teaching content that Chip taught in front of a live audience. This portion of the video is roughly 25 minutes in length. Finally, Chip will then share some closing thoughts and set up the discussion topics for your group.

3. **Be sure to test your video equipment ahead of time.** Practice using the equipment and make sure you have located this week's lesson on

the DVD menu. The video segments flow from one right into the next. So once you start the session, you won't have to stop the video until Chip has finished his closing thoughts and prepared the group for the first discussion question.

4. **Have enough materials on hand.** Before you start the video, make sure everyone has their own copy of the study guide. Encourage the group to open to this week's session and follow along with the teaching.

🕚 TALK IT OVER

Here are some guidelines for leading the discussion time:

1. **Make this a discussion, not a lecture.** Resist the temptation to do all the talking and to answer your own questions. Don't be afraid of a few moments of silence while people formulate their answers. And don't feel like you need to have all the answers. There is nothing wrong with simply responding "I don't know the answer to that, but I'll see if I can find an answer this week".

2. **Encourage everyone to participate.** Don't let one person dominate, but also don't pressure quieter members to speak during the first couple of sessions. After one person answers, don't immediately move on; ask what other people think, or say, "Would someone who hasn't shared like to add anything?"

3. **Affirm people's participation and input.** If an answer is clearly wrong, ask "What led you to that conclusion?" or ask what the rest of the group thinks. If a disagreement arises, don't be too quick to shut it down! The discussion can draw out important perspectives, and if you can't resolve it there, offer to research it further and return to the issue next week. However, if someone goes on the offensive and engages in personal attack of another person, you will need to step in as the leader. In the midst of spirited discussion, we must also remember that people are fragile and there is no place for disrespect.

4. **Detour when necessary.** If an important question is raised that is not in the study guide, take time to discuss it. Also, if someone shares something personal and emotional, take time for them. Stop and pray for them right then. Allow the Holy Spirit room to maneuver and follow His prompting when the discussion changes direction.

5. **Form subgroups.** One of the principles of small group life is "when numbers go up, sharing goes down". So, if you have a large group, sometimes you may want to split up into groups of 3-5 for discussion time. This is a great way to give everyone, even the quieter members, a chance to say something. Choose someone in the group to guide each of the smaller groups through the discussion. This involves others in the leadership of the group and provides an opportunity for training new leaders.

6. **Pray.** Be sensitive to the fact that some people in your group may be uncomfortable praying out loud. As a general rule, don't call on people to pray unless you have asked them ahead of time or have heard them pray in public. But this can also be a time to help people build their confidence to pray in a group. Consider having prayer times that ask people to just say a word or sentence of thanks to God.

⊙ LIVE IT OUT

These simple suggestions will help you apply the lesson. Be sure and leave adequate time to talk about practical applications of the lesson. This is a great way to build group community.

Try these ideas together and hold each other accountable for completing them, then share the following week how it went.

A FINAL WORD...

Keep an eye on the clock. Be sensitive to time. Whatever is the agreed upon time commitment, try to stick with it. It is always better to finish the meeting with people wanting more rather than people walking away stressed out because the meeting went long.

SESSION NOTES

Thanks for hosting this series called Balancing Life's Demands. This practical series will help you discover how to live a focused life amidst all the complexity of the 21st century. Whether you are brand new at leading a small group or you are a seasoned veteran, God is going to use you. God has a long history of using ordinary people like us to get His work done.

These brief notes are intended to help prepare you for each week's session. By spending just a few minutes each week previewing the video and going over these leader notes you will set the table for a great group experience. Also, don't forget to pray for your group each week.

SESSION 1
the peace and power of a prioritized life (1)   7

- If your group doesn't know each other well, be sure that you spend some time getting acquainted. Don't rush right into the video lesson. Remember, small groups are not just about a study or a meeting, they are about relationships.

- Be sure to capture everyone's contact information. It is a good idea to send out an e-mail (with permission) with everybody's contact information so that the group can stay in touch.

- When you are ready to start the session, be sure that each person in your group has a copy of the study guide. The small group study guide is important for people to follow along and to take notes.

- The video lesson taught by Chip Ingram will be about 25-30 minutes in length. So, you will have plenty of time for discussion. Each session opens with Chip setting up the lesson. Then, the video will transition to his live teaching. And, at the end of the teaching Chip will come back and wrap up the session as well as set up the first discussion question for the group.

- Facilitating the discussion time. Several times Chip will ask you as the facilitator to lead the way by answering the first question. This allows you to lead by example and your willingness to share openly about your life will help others feel the permission to do the same.

- Even though this is the first session, Chip will speak directly to the symptoms of misplaced priorities. If your group doesn't know each other very well, some of the questions in this session could feel a little intimidating. So, let people know it's ok to share only whatever they are comfortable sharing.

SESSION 2

the peace and power of a prioritized life (2)   13

- Why not begin your preparation by praying right now for the people in your group. You might even want to keep their names in your Bible. You may also want to ask people in your group how you can pray for them specifically.

- If somebody doesn't come back this week, be sure and follow up with them. Even if you knew they were going to have to miss the group meeting, give them a call or shoot them an e-mail letting them know that they were missed. It would also be appropriate to have a couple of other people in the group let them know they were missed.

- If you haven't already previewed the video, take the time to do so. It will help you know how to best facilitate the group and what are the best discussion questions for your group.

- One of the most important habits for growing Christians is learning how to spend time in God's word. Chip will provide a very practical and simple approach to study the Bible. The Live It Out challenge this week is for people to practice this method by spending 20 minutes a day for 5 days using the 2PROAPT on page 15. Challenge the group to give it a try.

SESSION 3

how to put "first things first" (1)   19

- Did anybody miss last week's session? If so, make it a priority to follow up and let them know they were missed. It just might be your care for them that keeps them connected to the group.

- Share the load. One of the ways to raise the sense of ownership within the group is to get them involved in more than coming to the meeting. So, get someone to help with refreshments... find somebody else to be in charge of the prayer requests... get someone else to be in charge of any social gathering you plan... let someone else lead the discussion one night. Give away as much of the responsibility as possible. That is GOOD leadership.

- Think about last week's meeting for a moment. Was there anyone that didn't talk or participate? In every group there are extroverts and there are introverts. There are people who like to talk and then there are those who are quite content NOT to talk. Not everyone engages in the same way or at the same level but you do want to try and create an environment where everyone wants to participate.

- Follow up with your group this week to see how they did in spending time in God's word. Find out what they experienced and learned from the 2PROAPT method. If some didn't give it a try, encourage them to try it this next week.

- In preparation for this week's session, go over the questions. Think about your own answers to the questions and be prepared to start the discussion if the group is slow to respond.

SESSION 4

how to put "first things first" (2)   25

- Don't feel any pressure to get through all the questions. As people open up and talk, don't move on too quickly. Give them the time to communicate their thoughts as they interact with this teaching.

- Don't be afraid of silence. When you ask people a question, give them time to think about it. Don't feel like you have to fill every quiet moment with words.

- If your group is not sharing as much as you would like or if the discussion is being dominated by a person or two, try subgrouping. If your group is 8 people or more, this is a great way to up the level of participation.

  After watching the video tape, divide the group into a couple of smaller groups for the discussion time. It is good to get someone you think would be a good facilitator to agree to this ahead of time

- One of the questions this week asks "if you were developing a 'to be' list, what would be on your list? If you have the time, come up with your list and be prepared to share it this week at your group meeting.

- For the Live It Out challenge this week, pass out some 3x5 cards to group members. Then, challenge them this week to write out the desires of their heart about who they want "to be".

SESSION 5
how to keep "first things first" (1)

- Confidentiality is crucial to group life. The moment trust is breached, people will shut down and close up. So, you may want to mention the importance of confidentiality again this week just to keep it on people's radar.

- Each time your group meets take a few minutes to update on what has happened since the last group meeting. Ask people what they are learning and putting into practice. Remember, being a disciple of Jesus means becoming a "doer of the word".

- This week's lesson is about biblical accountability. Accountability is a word that has been misused and misunderstood. Chip defines accountability as "enlisting the support of those who love me to help me keep my commitments to God." As your group discusses the lesson this week, keep the definition in front of them.

- This week the group will be challenged to use their Bibles to come up with a list of the "one anothers" of the Bible. In case some people don't bring their Bible, have a couple of extra Bibles that can be used for this exercise.

SESSION 6
how to keep "first things first" (2)

- You are now at the halfway point of this series. How is it going? How well is the group connecting? What has been going well and what needs a little work? Are there any adjustments you need to make?

- One way to deepen the level of community within your group is to spend time together outside the group meeting. If you have not already done so, plan something that will allow you to get to know each other better. Also, consider having someone else in the group take responsibility for your fellowship event.

- As you begin this week's session, do a check-in to see what people are learning and applying from this series. Don't be afraid to take some time at the beginning of your meeting to review some key ideas from the previous week's lessons.

- This week's lesson continues on the topic of accountability. One of the discussion questions asks people in the group to share a time when they benefited from a wound from a sincere friend. It would be good for you to lead out by sharing a story from your own life.

- Ask people this week to do the Live It Out challenge. The group will be asked to write out a list of accountability questions that would be helpful for someone to ask them.

SESSION 7

warning: personal discipline can be hazardous to your health (1) 45

- Consider asking someone in your group to facilitate next week's lesson. Who knows, there might be a great potential small group leader in your group. It will give you a break and give them a chance to grow.

- Consider sending an e-mail to each person in your group this week letting them know you prayed for them today. Also, let them know that you are grateful that they are in the group.

- The next several lessons come from Matthew 5 and 6. It would be helpful for you to take a few minutes to read these two chapters before your group meeting.

- This week is all about our righteousness exceeding that of the Pharisees. Consider getting on line and doing a little research about the Pharisees and their practices.

SESSION 8

warning: personal discipline can be hazardous to your health (2) 51

- Follow up questions. The only thing better than good questions are good follow up questions. Questions are like onions. Each question allows another layer to be peeled back and get beneath the surface.

- In your group meetings be sure to take adequate time for prayer. Don't just tack it on at the end of the meeting simply out of obligation. Also, don't be afraid to stop the meeting and pray for someone who shares a need or a struggle.

- During this week's session Chip will take some time to share the story of the cross. It is thorough and powerful. Let the group know that you would love to talk to anyone who has questions or wants to further explore what Chip was talking about.

- The Live It Out portion of this weeks lesson will challenge your group to do a 24 hour fast sometime in the next week. Chip will talk about fasting from Matthew 6. So, this is a great opportunity to give people a chance to try fasting. Challenge them not only to fast for a day but to take the time they normally spend eating and spend that time with God.

SESSION 9

- Since this is the next to the last week of this study, you might want to spend some time this week talking about what your group is going to do after your complete this study.

- As this series winds down, this is a good time to plan some kind of party or fellowship after you complete the study. Find the "party person" in your group and ask them to take on the responsibility of planning a fun experience for the group. Also, use this party as a time for people to share how God has used this series to grow them and change them.

- Chip is going to speak very directly about the issue of materialism among Christians. This topic might feel a little uncomfortable for some, but this topic is core to our discipleship. And, this teaching comes straight from the lips of Jesus.

SESSION 10

- Be sure that everyone is clear about what the group is doing next after this study.

- Don't forget to celebrate what God has been teaching you and doing in the lives of group members. You might want to take some time at the beginning of this week's session to have people share how this series has impacted them.

- Chip is going to take a portion of this session to talk about our self-inflicted busyness. This topic is absolutely crucial for Christian to balance the demands of life.

- The last question asks "What one change, if you actually made it, would help you live out what you have learned from this series?" Be sure to spend some time on this question. And, then spend time praying for one another asking God to give people the courage to put this series into action.

PRAYER AND PRAISE

One of the most important things you can do in your group is to pray with and for each other. Write down each other's concerns here so you can remember to pray for these requests during the week!

Use the Follow Up box to record an answer to a prayer or to write down how you might want to follow up with the person making the request. This could be a phone call, an e-mail, or a card. Your personal concern will mean a lot!

PERSON	PRAYER REQUEST	FOLLOW UP

PERSON	PRAYER REQUEST	FOLLOW UP

PERSON	PRAYER REQUEST	FOLLOW UP

PERSON	PRAYER REQUEST	FOLLOW UP

PERSON	PRAYER REQUEST	FOLLOW UP

PERSON	PRAYER REQUEST	FOLLOW UP

GROUP ROSTER

NAME	HOME PHONE	EMAIL

WHAT'S NEXT?

More Group Studies from Chip Ingram

NEW BIO
Quench Your Thirst for Life

5 video sessions

Cinematic story illustrates Biblical truth in this 5-part video study that unlocks the Biblical DNA for spiritual momentum by examining the questions at the heart of true spirituality.

NEW House or Home Marriage
God's Blueprint for a Great Marriage

10 video sessions

The foundational building blocks of marriage are crumbling before our eyes, and Christians aren't exempt. It's time to go back to the blueprint and examine God's plan for marriages that last for a lifetime.

NEW Good to Great in God's Eyes
10 Practices Great Christians Have in Common

10 video sessions

If you long for spiritual breakthrough, take a closer look at ten powerful practices that will rekindle a fresh infusion of faith and take you from good to great...in God's eyes.

Balancing Life's Demands
Biblical Priorities for Busy Lives

10 video sessions

Busy, tired and stressed out? Learn how to put "first things first" and find peace in the midst of pressure and adversity.

Effective Parenting in a Defective World
Raising Kids that Stand Out from the Crowd

9 video sessions

Packed with examples and advice for raising kids, this series presents Biblical principles for parenting that still work today.

Experiencing God's Dream for Your Marriage
Practical Tools for a Thriving Marriage

12 video sessions

Examine God's design for marriage and the real life tools and practices that will transform it for a lifetime.

Five Lies that Ruin Relationships
Building Truth-Based Relationships

10 video sessions

Uncover five powerful lies that wreck relationships and experience the freedom of understanding how to recognize God's truth.

The Genius of Generosity
Lessons from a Secret Pact Between Friends

4 video sessions

The smartest financial move you can make is to invest in God's Kingdom. Learn His design for wise giving and generous living.

God As He Longs for You To See Him
Getting a Right View of God

10 video sessions

A deeper look at seven attributes of God's character that will change the way you think, pray and live.

Holy Ambition
Turning God-Shaped Dreams Into Reality

7 video sessions

Do you long to turn a God-inspired dream into reality? Learn how God uses everyday believers to accomplish extraordinary things.

Invisible War
The Believer's Guide to Satan, Demons & Spiritual Warfare

8 video sessions

Are you "battle ready"? Learn how to clothe yourself with God's "spiritual armor" and be confident of victory over the enemy of your soul.

Living On The Edge
Becoming a Romans 12 Christian

10 video sessions

If God exists...what does he want from us? Discover the profile of a healthy disciple and learn how to experience God's grace.

Watch previews & order at www.LivingontheEdge.org

Love, Sex & Lasting Relationships

God's Prescription to Enhance Your Love Life

10 video sessions

Do you believe in "true love"? Discover a better way to find love, stay in love, and build intimacy that lasts a lifetime.

The Miracle of Life Change

How to Change for Good

10 video sessions

Ready to make a change? Explore God's process of true transformation and learn to spot barriers that hold you back from receiving God's best.

Overcoming Emotions that Destroy

Constructive Tools for Destructive Emotions

10 video sessions

We all struggle with destructive emotions that can ruin relationships. Learn God's plan to overcome angry feelings for good.

Rebuilding Your Broken World

How God Puts Broken Lives Back Together

8 video sessions

Starting over? Learn how God can reshape your response to trials and bring healing to broken relationships and difficult circumstances.

Why I Believe

Answers to Life's Most Difficult Questions

12 video sessions

Examine the Biblical truth behind the pivotal questions at the heart of human existence and the claims of the Christian faith.

Your Divine Design

Discover, Develop and Deploy Your Spiritual Gifts

8 video sessions

How has God uniquely wired you? Discover God's purpose for spiritual gifts and how to identify your own.

Watch previews & order at www.LivingontheEdge.org